THE
COTSW

A WALK

The Green, Broadway

The Devil's Chimney, Leckhampton Hill

THE
COTSWOLD WAY

A WALKERS' GUIDE

MARK RICHARDS

Tithe Barn, Stanway

Published by
THORNHILL PRESS
Cheltenham

Published by Thornhill Press

© Mark B. Richards

ISBN 0 904110 931

1st Impression March 1973
2nd Impression September 1973
3rd Impression September 1974
4th Impression April 1977
2nd Edition February 1979
Reprinted (amended) January 1980
3rd (revised) Edition 1982
Reprinted (amended) 1984

Printed by Logos Ltd, Cinderford

To
AW and Betty

Sheppey Corner, Stanton

ACKNOWLEDGEMENTS

Now that this book is in its third fully revised edition as a result of the continuing success of the Guide and the Way, I would like to record my grateful thanks to those who have helped me, in particular:

To Mr. Antony J. Drake (Rambler's Association, Footpath Secretary Gloucestershire Area) who has kept me on the right path and been willing at all times to render valuable help and advice. To Mr. Cyril Trenfield (Ramblers' Association, Footpath Secretary, Avon) who in a similar capacity has given assistance. Also, to the Gloucestershire County Council for their help in ensuring I did not stray.

Finally, but not least, to my mother and father whose enthusiasm has encouraged me most of all.

Thank you, one and all.

M.B.R.

NOTE

Whilst every possible care has been taken to ensure the accuracy of the information contained in this Guide, neither the Author nor Publishers accept any liability regarding the information contained herein or its interpretation by readers.

The Author recommends that a copy of the Country Code be obtained and the rules therein followed. Please remember, you cross private land as a privilege, so do not abuse it and spoil it for those who may follow you.

CONTENTS

The Happy Valley backed by Cleeve Common

CHIPPING CAMPDEN 'WOOL' CHURCH

FOREWORD

Since the first edition of this guide was published in 1973, the Cotswold Way has become firmly established as one of Britain's most popular non official long distance paths. This is mainly due to the attractiveness of its scenery and the wide vistas it commands from the top of the Cotswold escarpment. Its popularity is, however, in no small measure also due to Mark Richards whose walkers' guide has portrayed the route and the features alongside it in the attractive style of Alfred Wainwright. Mark wisely sought and received advice from the author of the unique Lake District guidebooks, in order to develop his artistic abilities, and now, with two further long distance paths guides to his credit he has established his own style of strip map portrayal and feature illustration. The 35,000 copies printed to date give testimony to the popularity of this guide and its form of presentation, which avoids the tedium of following a stile by stile description of the route.

Many who have walked the Cotswold Way have questioned why it is not a national footpath and why some routes of less attraction have received official recognition with consequent 100% grants for creating new rights of way, path improvements and publicity. To explain this it is necessary to trace the history of the project to date. Following the passing of the National Parks and Access to the Countryside Act of 1949, which made provision for the designation and creation of long distance paths, I put forward the idea of a footpath route following the Cotswold escarpment. This met with great interest but the plans which the Gloucestershire Committee of the Ramblers Association submitted to the National Parks Commission in 1953, though acknowledged and mentioned in the Commission's annual report of that year, were nevertheless pigeonholed and largely forgotten until Gloucestershire County Council prepared its recreational plan for the countryside in 1968. The County Council decided to designate a Cotswold Way route itself, using existing public rights of way, and the scheme was launched during Footpath Week in May 1970. The Way had priority in the county's first path signposting programme and in 1975 "Operation Cotswaymark" was launched. Members of the Cotswold Warden Service and the Ramblers Association obtained permission from over a hundred landowners to waymark the whole way in both directions, using the Countryside Commission's code of painted yellow arrows for footpaths and blue for bridleways. White arrows were put where the Way had to follow roads and a white spot was put alongside all arrows as the symbol for the Cotswold Way. A team of thirty volunteers maintains the waymarking and carries out path improvements. Alas the Cotswold Way is now unlikely to receive official designation as the Countryside Commission slows down its designation programme. The Way could however qualify for 50% grant as a recreational footpath, particularly for creating new rights of way to avoid dangerous road sections. The lack of national designation should not deter prospective walkers of the Cotswold Way, who can be assured of a delightful and rewarding experience, following the route with this guidebook and the waymarking.

Antony J. Drake
Cheltenham December 1979

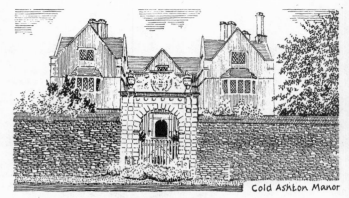

Cold Ashton Manor

INTRODUCTION

The Cotswold Way as a walkers' route is a splendid expedition of nearly one hundred miles. Accompanying the Cotswold escarpment, adhering to established footpaths and bridleways, it is rich enough in variety to interest any walker, whether hardened rambler or member of a family group.

The Cotswold Way can be looked upon as a seven to nine day expedition for any normally active person. For many, however, circumstances may prevent the completion of the route in one continuous walk: for them armed with this Guide, it can be savoured in manageable sections. This Guide is designed to facilitate an either-way passage, although it has been necessary, for a natural sequence of the strip-map, to start the walk at Chipping Campden and to follow it through the book to finish at Bath. However, many may consider that a northward passage is more desirable; in so doing the prevailing south-westerly weather is to one's back and as the escarpment grows in stature, so the more distinctive of Cotswold scenery unfolds ahead. In order that the walker can plan his walk, it is of paramount importance to carry the relevant 1:50,000 Ordnance Survey maps (as indicated Page 72). Five are needed for the whole walk; these can be of great assistance as they give a much broader picture of the surrounding country than is possible herein. The maps in this Guide possess only those features considered essential to the walker primarily engaged on the Cotswold Way.

The Cotswolds are part of a continuous belt of limestone lying between the River Humber and the Dorsetshire coast and attaining its greatest height and breadth throughout its course with the Oolitic Limestone of the Cotswold Hills. These are not hills in an individual sense, being a scarp/dip formation. The steep western escarpment forming a wall to the Evesham and Severn Vales is but an abrupt termination of high wold country, gently dipping to the south-east to merge ultimately with the Oxford plain.

For those whose quest is for pleasant rambling the Cotswold Way introduces all the elements distinctive of Cotswold country, gains aquaintance with a string of lovely villages that lie near or in the shelter of the escarpment, and visits many features of historical interest. The walks along woodland ways, the following of enchanting paths in the company of the escarpment with its far-ranging views over valley and plain to Malvern and distant Shropshire heights and the mountains of South Wales, the delights of rural scenes and quiet villages, the song of birds and the rustle of leaves reflecting the peace and tranquility of a lovely countryside – these are the joys that await the walker along the Cotswold Way.

The route, as described in this Guide, begins at Chipping Campden, in Gloucestershire, one of the finest of the old Cotswold market towns. Situated at the northern end of the Cotswold escarpment, this makes a fitting starting point for the Cotswold Way. A place of rare charm and beauty, Chipping Campden is rich in the mellow stone architecture for which the Cotswolds are justly famous, a heritage from days when sheep brought prosperity to Gloucestershire and wealthy wool merchants settled there. The route bids farewell to the final vestiges of the escarpment as it descends by parkland, street and alleyway to finish at the very heart of the beautiful Roman City of Bath, in Avon, famed for its elegant Regency houses, streets and terraces, but most of all for the wonderfully preserved relics of Roman occupation – making a fitting end to a walk full of character, interest and beauty: the Cotswold Way.

Twelve years have passed since the Cotswold Way was formally established and during this time it has rooted itself firmly into the fabric of the Cotswold landscape. A happy idea of Tony Drake's in the 1950's became a reality in 1970 and now here in the 1980's became a practical recreational amenity.

With the new edition of this particular guide, the route can clearly be seen to have matured. Minor embellishments have and will continue to be made but walkers can luxuriate in a waymarking system that reflects a high level of care and constant attention. Throughout the route 'Operation Cotswaymark', a project run jointly by the Cotswold A.O.N.B. Warden Service and the Ramblers' Association, ensures walkers need not stray. To the nationally adopted system to distinguish rights of way – Yellow arrow: Footpath, Blue arrow: Bridleway is added a white spot to confirm the Cotswold Way linear walk. In addition on roads a white arrow has been employed with the white spot. The Cotswold Way is maintained by the Cotswold A.O.N.B. Warden Service, a practical service coordinated and administered from Shire Hall, Gloucester, by the Head Warden. Voluntary Wardens are always in demand and many come from the ranks of walkers to assist in positively with work on rights of way or in guiding visitors. If you should encounter any obstructions or difficulties en route, please direct your observations to the Head Warden.

I have never ceased to take pleasure from treading those familiar paths, delving through the pastures and woods that clothe the Cotswold edge, enjoying the unfolding seasons of the Cotswold year.

So to all who walk the Cotswold Way may I wish the very best of walking days, and many a serene beauty to fill those pleasurable hours. Treasure them.

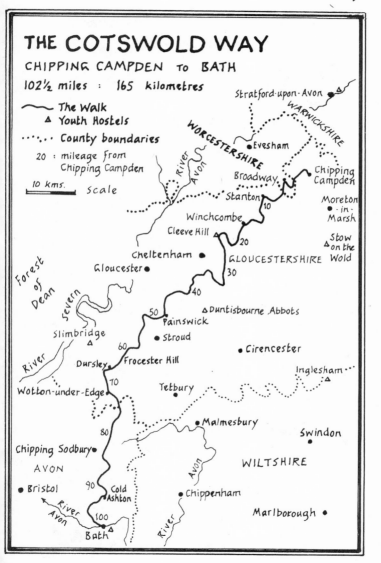

THE COTSWOLD WAY

CHIPPING CAMPDEN TO BATH

102½ miles : 165 kilometres

~~~ The Walk
△ Youth Hostels
······ County boundaries
20 : mileage from
     Chipping Campden

10 kms.   Scale

Stratford-upon-Avon △

WARWICKSHIRE

WORCESTERSHIRE

Evesham

River Avon

Broadway   Chipping Campden

Stanton   10

Moreton -in- Marsh

Winchcombe

Cleeve Hill   20

Cheltenham ●

Stow on the Wold △

GLOUCESTERSHIRE

Gloucester ●

Forest of Dean

Severn

30

40

50   Painswick

△ Duntisbourne Abbots

● Stroud

● Cirencester

Slimbridge △

River

60

Dursley   Frocester Hill

70

Tetbury

Inglesham △

Wotton-under-Edge

80

● Malmesbury

Swindon ●

Chipping Sodbury ●

AVON

● Bristol

90   Cold Ashton

WILTSHIRE

Avon

● Chippenham

River Avon

100

Bath △

Marlborough ●

River

View east along the escarpment of Dover's Hill to Meon Hill 635'

Grevel's House

The Fish Inn

Woolstapler's Hall Museum

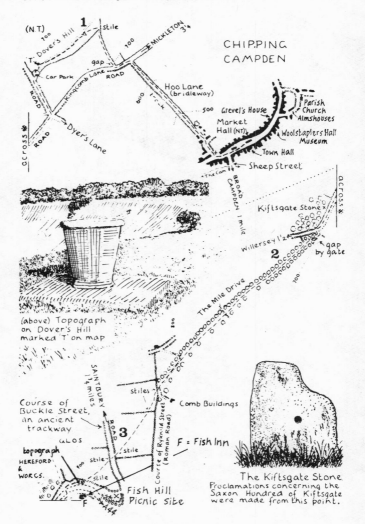

CHIPPING CAMPDEN

(N.T)

1

stile

Dover's Hill

T. Dover's Hill

gap

Car Park

Kingcomb Lane

ROAD

MICKLETON 3x

Hoo Lane
(bridleway)

Grevel's House

Market
Hall (N.T)

Parish
Church
Almshouses

Woolstaplers Hall
Museum

Town Hall

across

ROAD

Dyer's Lane

ROAD

Sheep Street

The Cam

BROAD CAMPDEN 1 mile

across

Kiftsgate Stone

Willersey 1½

gap
by gate

2

The Mile Drive

(above) Topograph
on Dover's Hill
marked T on map

SAINTBURY 1¼ miles

stiles

Comb Buildings

Course of
Buckle Street,
an ancient
trackway

GLOS.

topograph

HEREFORD
& WORCS.

3

stile

stile

stile

Course of Ryknild Street (Roman Road)

F = Fish Inn

Fish Hill
Picnic Site

F

The Kiftsgate Stone.
Proclamations concerning the
Saxon Hundred of Kiftsgate
were made from this point.

C15th Cottages, High Street
Broadway

The Lygon Arms
a C16th coaching inn, beautifully restored early C20th

THE FISH INN to BROADWAY

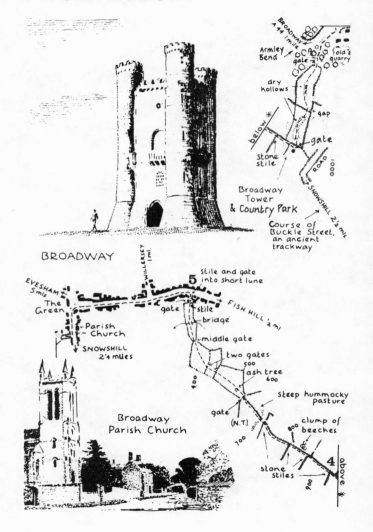

Broadway Tower & Country Park

Course of Buckle Street, an ancient trackway

A44 ½ mile Broadway

Armley Bend

gate

old quarry

dry hollows

gap

below

gate

stone stile

ROAD 1000

SNOWSHILL 2½ mls

BROADWAY

EVESHAM 5 mls

WILLERSEY 1 ml

The Green

Parish Church

SNOWSHILL 2¼ miles

stile and gate into short lane

5

FISH HILL 2 ml

gate

stile

bridge

middle gate

two gates

500

ash tree 600

400

steep hummocky pasture

gate (N.T.)

clump of beeches

800

700

stone stiles

900

4

above

Broadway Parish Church

Stanton from Shenberrow Hill

Guildhouse

Shenberrow Camp

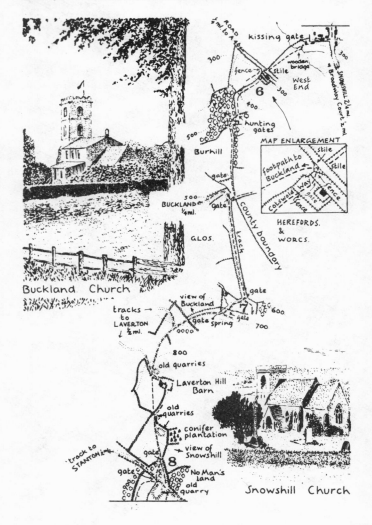

ROAD to A.44

kissing gate

300

fence

wooden bridge

stile

West End

SNOWSHILL 2¼ ml
Broadway Court 2 ml

6

400

hunting gates

Burhill

500

gate

500
BUCKLAND ¼ ml.

gate

County Boundary

track

GLOS.

Buckland Church

MAP ENLARGEMENT

footpath to Buckland

stile

stile

Cotswold Way

gate

fence

fence

HEREFORDS.
&
WORCS.

view of
Buckland

gate

tracks →
to
LAVERTON
↓ ½ ml.

gate
spring

gate

7

600

700

800
old quarries

Laverton Hill
Barn

old
quarries

conifer
plantation

view of
Snowshill

track to
STANTON ½ ml.

gate

gate

8

No Man's
land
old
quarry

Snowshill Church

Stanton

LONG HILL PLANTATION to STANWAY

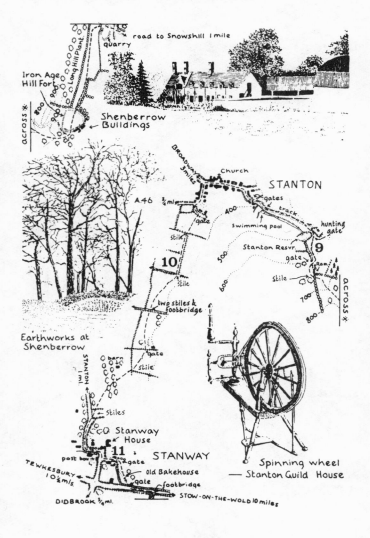

road to Snowshill 1 mile

quarry

Long Hill Plant.

Iron Age Hill Fort

across ✱

800

Shenberrow
← Buildings

Broadway 3 miles

Church

STANTON

A46 ¼ml

gates

track

gate

400

hunting gate

swimming pool

stile

Stanton Resvr

10

500

gate

9

Ram

stile

stile

600

700

across ✱

800

two stiles & footbridge

Earthworks at Shenberrow

barn

STANTON 1ml

gate

stile

stiles

Stanway House

post box

11 gate STANWAY

TEWKESBURY 10½mls

Old Bakehouse

gate footbridge

DIDBROOK ¾ml.

→ STOW-ON-THE-WOLD 10 miles

Spinning wheel
— Stanton Guild House

Beckbury Hill Fort

St. Faiths, Farmcote

STANWAY to HAILES WOOD

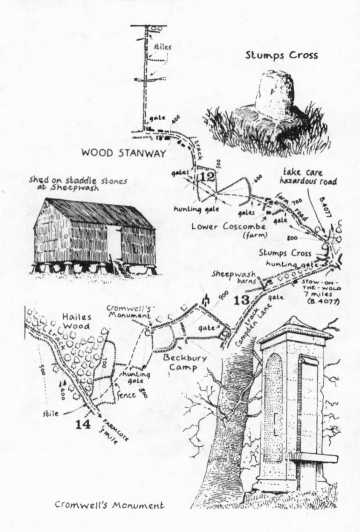

stiles

Stumps Cross

gate   400

WOOD STANWAY   track

gates   **12**   500

hunting gate   gates   gate   farm 700 road   B.4077

Lower Coscombe
(farm)

shed on staddle stones
at Sheepwash

200

Stumps Cross
hunting gate

Sheepwash barns   STOW-ON-THE-WOLD 7 miles (B.4077)

13   gate   track

900

Cromwell's Monument

Hailes Wood

track

500   gate   Campden Lane

Beckbury Camp

400   hunting gate

fence

stile   **14**   FARMCOTE ½mile

Cromwell's Monument

Amid the peaceful ruins of Hailes Abbey, founded in 1246 A.D.

HAILES WOOD TO WINCHCOMBE

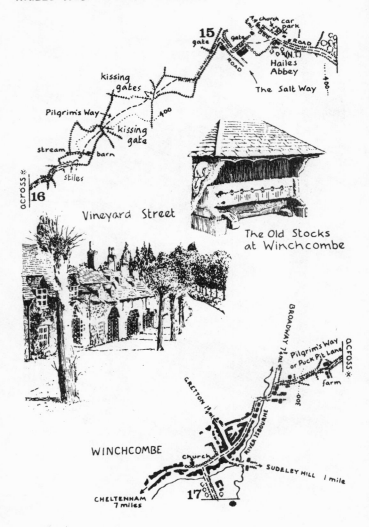

15

gate

church car park

gate

ROAD

(N.T.)

Hailes Abbey

→ The Salt Way

kissing gates

400

Pilgrim's Way

kissing gate

stream

barn

stiles

ACROSS ✳

16

Vineyard Street

The Old Stocks at Winchcombe

BROADWAY 7½m

Pilgrim's Way or Puck Pit Lane

ACROSS ✳

farm

300

GRETTON 1½m

RIVER ISBOURNE

WINCHCOMBE

Church

SUDELEY HILL 1 mile

CHELTENHAM 7 miles

17

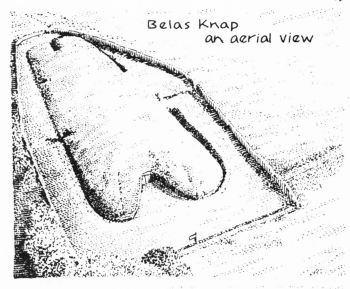

Belas Knap
an aerial view

N.E. Chamber

WINCHCOMBE to WONTLEY FARM

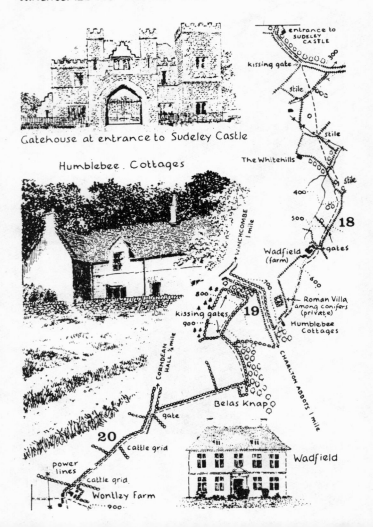

Gatehouse at entrance to Sudeley Castle

Humblebee Cottages

entrance to
SUDELEY
CASTLE

kissing gate

stile

stile

The Whitehills

stile

400

500

18

Wadfield
(farm)

gates

600

Roman Villa
among conifers
(private)

Humblebee
Cottages

WINCHCOMBE
1 mile

800

kissing gates

19

900

CORNDEAN HALL ½ mile

CHARLTON ABBOTS 1 mile

Belas Knap

gate

20

cattle grid

power
lines

cattle grid

Wontlzy Farm

900

Wadfield

Castle Rock

Cleeve Cloud Hill Fort

Cleeve Cloud

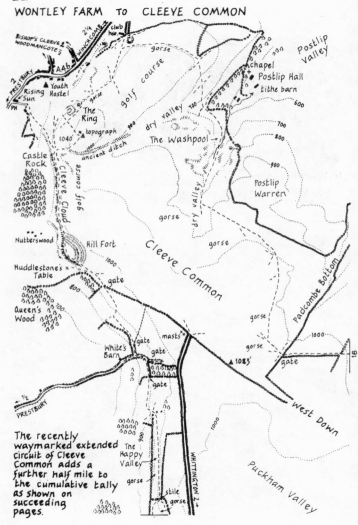

BISHOP'S CLEEVE 2
WOODMANCOTE 2
2¼ LINHCOMBE
club hse
A4b
2 PRESTBURY
Rising Sun
▲ Youth Hostel
¹/₁ PH
gorse
golf course
chapel
Postlip Hall
tithe barn
Postlip Valley
600
The Ring
topograph
1040
ancient ditch
gorse
900
dry valley
The Washpool
700
700
800
900
Castle Rock
Cleeve Cloud
gorse
dry valley
Postlip Warren
Nutterswood
Hill Fort
1000
gorse
gorse
Cleeve Common
gorse
Huddlestone's Table
gate
800
Queen's Wood
700
gate
masts
gate
gorse
1000
Padcombe Bottom
gate
White's Barn
▲ 1083'
18
½ PRESTBURY
gate
West Down
900
1000
The Happy Valley
WHITTINGTON 2
Puckham Valley
gorse
stile
gorse

The recently waymarked extended circuit of Cleeve Common adds a further half mile to the cumulative tally as shown on succeeding pages.

The A.40 passing Dowdeswell Reservoir overlooked by the village of Dowdeswell.

CLEEVE COMMON to DOWDESWELL RESVR.

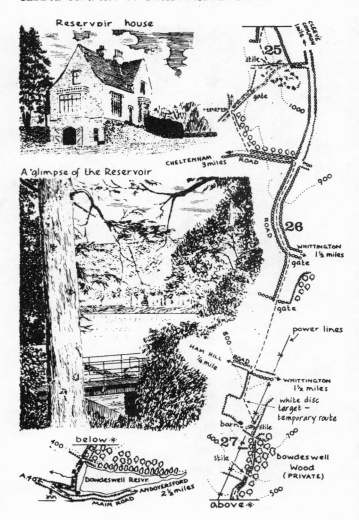

Reservoir house

CLEEVE COMMON STILE

25

stile

gate

1000

CHELTENHAM 3miles ROAD

900

A glimpse of the Reservoir

ROAD

26

WHITTINGTON 1½ miles

gate

gate

power lines

HAM HILL ¼ mile ROAD

WHITTINGTON 1½ miles

white disc target — temporary route

barn

stile

27

stile

Dowdeswell Wood (PRIVATE)

700

600

500

below ✳

400

A40

Dowdeswell Resvr.

MAIN ROAD   ANDOVERSFORD 2½ miles

above ✳

Ravensgate Hill

Seven Springs

The re-routing of the Cotswold Way off Chatcombe Pitch has added a little over one mile and certainly upgraded this section, despite the pylons near Needlehole!

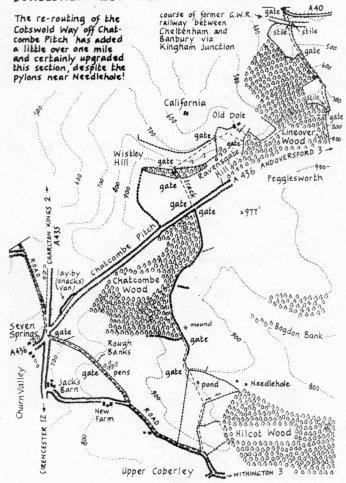

course of former G.W.R. railway between Cheltenham and Banbury via Kingham Junction

A40

gate

stile   stile

gate   500

600

California

Old Dole

stile

Lineover Wood

gate   800

700

Wistley Hill

gate

gate

Ravensgate Hill

A 436 ANDOVERSFORD 3

900

Pegglesworth

gate

track

gate

gate

× 977′

CHARLTON KINGS 2

A435

Chatcombe Pitch

lay-by (snacks) (van)

Chatcombe Wood

× mound

gate

900

Bogdon Bank

Seven Springs

A436

gate

Rough Banks

gate   pens

gate

pond

• Needlehole   800

Jack's Barn

Churn Valley

New Farm

ROAD

900

Hilcot Wood

CIRENCESTER 12

800

Upper Coberley   WITHINGTON 3

The Devil's Chimney
Leckhampton Hill

CHARLTON KINGS COMMON TO BARROW WAKE

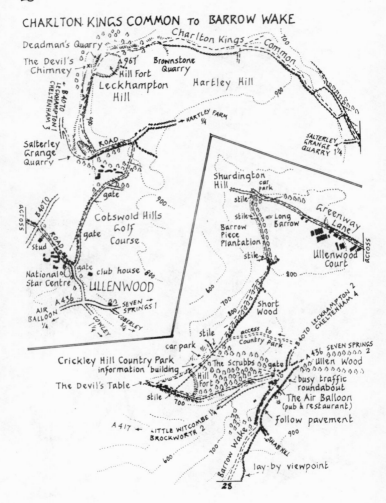

Deadman's Quarry

Charlton Kings Common

The Devil's Chimney

961 Hill Fort

Brownstone Quarry

Leckhampton Hill

Hartley Hill

B4070 LECKHAMPTON/ CHELTENHAM 3

HARTLEY FARM 1/4

Salterley Grange Quarry

ROAD

SALTERLEY GRANGE QUARRY 1 1/4

ACROSS

B4070

ROAD

gate

Cotswold Hills Golf Course

900

Shurdington Hill

car park

stile

stile

Greenway Lane

W.H. Long Barrow

Barrow Piece Plantation

Ullenwood Court

stile

stud

gate

gate

club house

National Star Centre

ULLENWOOD

A436

SEVEN SPRINGS 1

AIR BALLOON 1/4

COWLEY 1/4

COBERLEY 3/4

800

600

700

Short Wood

900

stile

B4070 LECKHAMPTON 2 CHELTENHAM 4

stile

access to Country Park

A436 SEVEN SPRINGS 2

Ullen Wood

car park

Crickley Hill Country Park information building

The Scrubbs

gate

Hill Fort

busy traffic roundabout

The Air Balloon (pub & restaurant)

The Devil's Table

stile

700

Follow pavement

A417

LITTLE WITCOMBE 1/4 BROCKWORTH 2

SHAB HILL

900

600

700

Barrow Wake

lay-by viewpoint

Crickley Hill

BARROW WAKE to COOPER'S HILL

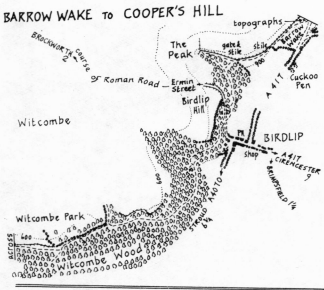

BROCKWORTH 2

Course of Roman Road — Ermin Street

The Peak

topographs

gate & stile

stile

Barrow Wake

700

A 417

Cuckoo Pen

Birdlip Hill

Witcombe

600

STROUD A4070

PH

shop

BIRDLIP

A 417 CIRENCESTER 9

BRIMPSFIELD 1¼

Witcombe Park

600

Across

Witcombe Wood

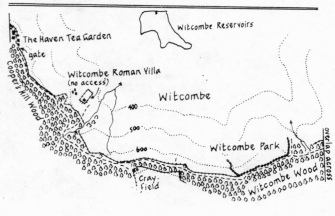

Witcombe Reservoirs

The Haven Tea Garden

gate

Coopers Hill Wood

Witcombe Roman Villa
(no access)

Witcombe

400

500

600

Witcombe Park

overlap across

Cray field

Witcombe Wood

Cooper's Hill

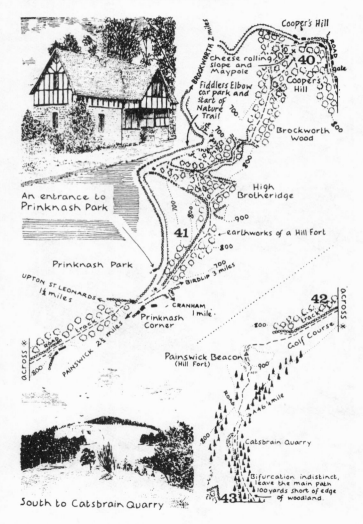

An entrance to
Prinknash Park

Prinknash Park

South to Catsbrain Quarry

Cooper's Hill

BROCKWORTH 2 miles

cheese rolling
slope and
Maypole

40

Cooper's
Hill

ROAD

gate

Fiddlers Elbow
car park and
start of
Nature
Trail

700

700

Brockworth
Wood

800

High
Brotheridge

700

800

900

41

← earthworks of a Hill Fort

800

700

BIRDLIP 3 miles

UPTON ST LEONARDS
1¼ miles

CRANHAM
1 mile

track

Prinknash
Corner

PAINSWICK 2½ miles

across ✕

ROAD

800

42

across ✕

track

800

Golf Course

Painswick Beacon
(Hill Fort)

900

ROAD

A.A.B. ½ mile

800

Catsbrain Quarry

Bifurcation indistinct,
leave the main path
100 yards short of edge
of woodland.

43

Painswick from Edgemoor Inn

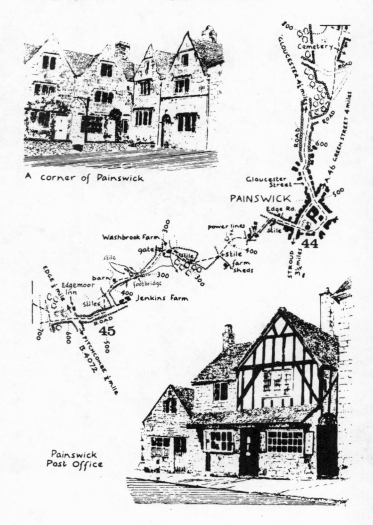

A corner of Painswick

Cemetery

Gloucester 4½ miles

ROAD

A 46 GREEN STREET 4 miles

600

Gloucester Street

PAINSWICK

Edge Rd.

stile

44

STROUD 3¾ miles

power lines

stile

400

stile

farm sheds

Washbrook Farm

gate

300

stile

300

stile

barn

footbridge

300

Edge Road

Edgemoor Inn

stiles

400

ROAD

Jenkins Farm

45

PITCHCOMBE ½ mile

B 4072

Painswick Post Office

The well, Cliffwell House

O.S. Column
Haresfield Beacon

The hexagonal house

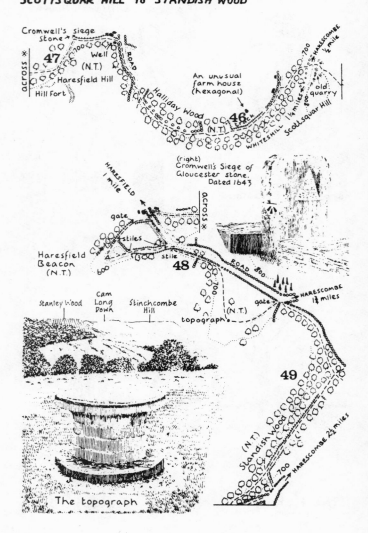

Cromwell's siege stone

47

Well (N.T.)

Haresfield Hill

Hill Fort

across X

HARESCOMBE ½ mile

ROAD

700

old quarry

An unusual farm house (hexagonal)

Halliday Wood (N.T.)

46

WHITESHILL 1¼ miles

Scottsquar Hill

(right)
Cromwell's Siege of
Gloucester stone.
Dated 1643

HARESFIELD 1 mile

across X

gate

stiles

stile

Haresfield
Beacon
(N.T.)

600

48

ROAD 700

HARESCOMBE 1¼ miles

gate

Stanley Wood

Cam Long Down

Stinchcombe Hill

topograph (N.T.)

49

Standish Wood (N.T.)

700

HARESCOMBE 2¼ miles

The topograph

2 bridges at Ryeford

Stroudwater Canal

River Frome

STANDISH WOOD TO RYEFORD

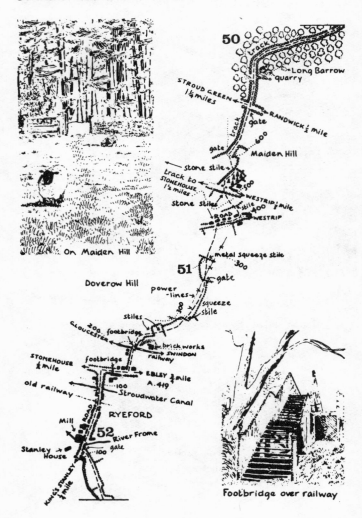

On Maiden Hill

50

track

Long Barrow

quarry

STROUD GREEN
1½ miles

gate   RANDWICK ½ mile

track   600

gate

Maiden Hill

stone stile

track to
STONEHOUSE
1½ miles   stile   500

WESTRIP ½ mile

stone stile   400

ROAD   WESTRIP

metal squeeze stile
300

51   gate

Doverow Hill   power
—lines—   squeeze
stile

stiles   8

20a   footbridges
GLOUCESTER

brick works
railway   SWINDON

STONEHOUSE   footbridge
½ mile
EBLEY ¾ mile
A.419

old railway   100
Stroudwater Canal

RYEFORD

Mill

52   River Frome

Stanley   gate
House   100

KINGS STANLEY
½ mile

Footbridge over railway

Penn Lane

King's Stanley Church

RYEFORD to BUCKHOLT WOOD

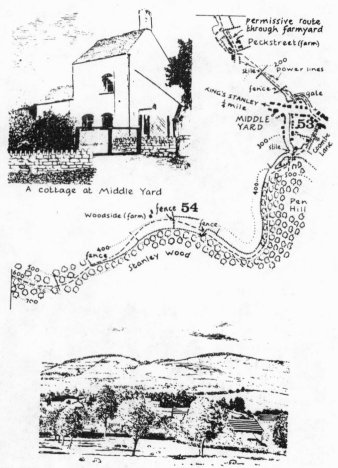

A cottage at Middle Yard

permissive route
through farmyard
Peckstreet (farm)

stile
200 Power lines
fence
gate
KING'S STANLEY ¼ mile

MIDDLE YARD
53
Combe Lane
300 stile
2nd
500
400
Pen Hill

Woodside (farm) fence 54
fence
400 fence
500
600 Stanley Wood
700

View on Middle Yard with Doverow Hill and Standish Wood

Uleybury

Cam Long Down

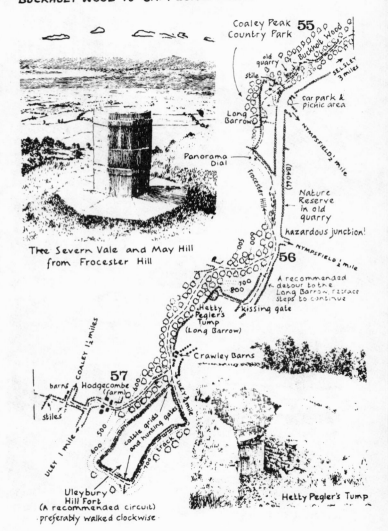

The Severn Vale and May Hill from Frocester Hill

Coaley Peak Country Park **55**

Buckholt Wood

old quarry

stile

SELSLEY 3 miles

car park & picnic area

Long Barrow

NYMPSFIELD ½ mile

Panorama Dial

Frocester Hill (B4066)

Nature Reserve in old quarry

hazardous junction!

NYMPSFIELD ½ mile

500

56

600

700

800

A recommended detour to the Long Barrow, retrace steps to continue

Hetty Pegler's Tump (Long Barrow)

kissing gate

Crawley Barns

Uley ½ mile

COALEY 1½ miles

barns

Hodgecombe (farm)

57

600

stiles

ULEY 1 mile

500

cattle grids and hunting gates

700

old track

Uleybury Hill Fort (A recommended circuit) preferably walked clockwise

Hetty Pegler's Tump

Market House in Dursley,
built in 1738, with statue
of Queen Anne

Owlpen Manor
near Uley

44

CAM LONG DOWN TO STANCOMBE PARK

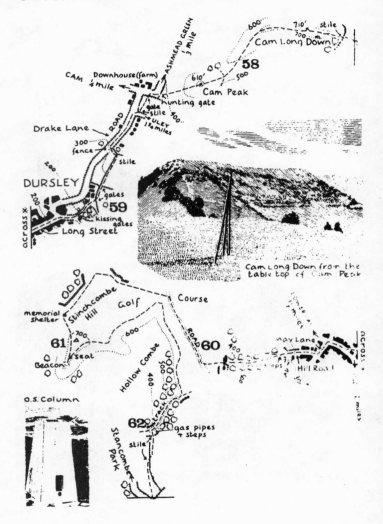

Cam Long Down from the table top of Cam Peak

O.S. Column

Nibley Knoll

North-eastward from the Tyndale Monument gallery

| CAM LONG DOWN | COALEY PEAK | DOWNHAM HILL | ULEYBURY HILL FORT |

STANCOMBE PARK TO WOTTON HILL

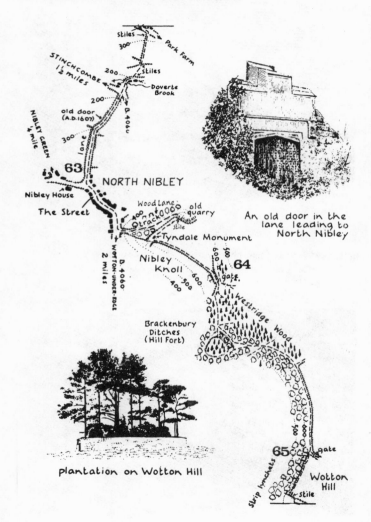

Stiles
300
200
Park Farm
Stiles
Doverte Brook
STINCHCOMBE 1½ miles
200
old door (A.D.1607)
300
B.4060
lane
NIBLEY GREEN ¼ mile
63
NORTH NIBLEY
Nibley House
The Street
Wood Lane
track
old quarry
Stile
Tyndale Monument
Nibley Knoll
400
500
600
600
500
400
64
gate
WOTTON-UNDER-EDGE 2 miles
B.4060
Brackenbury Ditches (Hill Fort)
Westridge Wood
500
65
gate
Strip lynchets
Wotton Hill
stile

An old door in the lane leading to North Nibley

plantation on Wotton Hill

Wotton - under - Edge Church.

Wortley

WOTTON HILL TO ALDERLEY

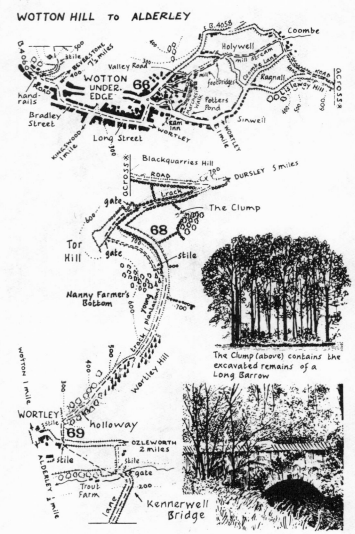

B.4058

BEVERSTONE 7½ miles

500

WOTTON UNDER-EDGE

66

Valley Road

Holywell

Coombe

B.4058

400

300

mill stream

Coombe Lane

Ragnall

mill

footbridges

Sinwell

Potters Pond

Marraw's Walk

Lisleway Hill

ROAD

LANE

A.CROSS.*

400 500 600

hand-rails

ROAD

KINGSWOOD 1 mile

Bradley Street

Long Street

500

Ram Inn

WORTLEY

WORTLEY 1 mile

ACROSS

Blackquarries Hill

ROAD

700

CX

DURSLEY 5 miles

track

gate

600

The Clump

68

Tor Hill

700

gate

stile

Nanny Farmer's Bottom

0.00

700

track, 1 plantation

young

Wortley Hill

WOTTON 1 mile

500

400

300

WORTLEY

stile

69

holloway

OZLEWORTH 2 miles

stile

stile

ALDERLEY 2 miles

ALDERLEY 2 mile

Trout Farm

gate

200

lane

Kennerwell Bridge

The Clump (above) contains the excavated remains of a Long Barrow

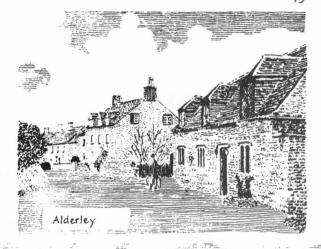

Alderley

Kilcott Mill

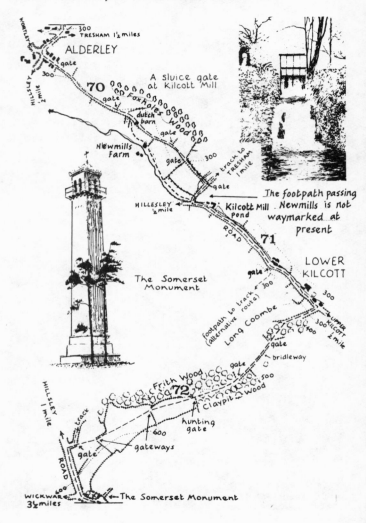

WORTLEY 1½ miles

300

TRESHAM 1½ miles

ALDERLEY

gate

HILLSLEY ½ mile

300

70

A sluice gate
at Kilcott Mill

gate

Foxholes

dutch barn

Wood

gate

Newmills Farm

gate

300

track to TRESHAM 1 mile

gate

HILLESLEY ½ mile

Kilcott Mill
pond

The footpath passing
Newmills is not
waymarked at
present

ROAD

71

LOWER
KILCOTT

gate

300

The Somerset
Monument

300

UPPER KILCOTT 2 mile

footpath to track
(alternative route)

Long Coombe

gate

bridleway

gate

Frith Wood

gate

72

500

Claypit Wood

HILLSLEY 1 mile

track

600

hunting gate

gateways

gate

ROAD

600

WICKWAR
3½ miles

The Somerset Monument

Horton Church

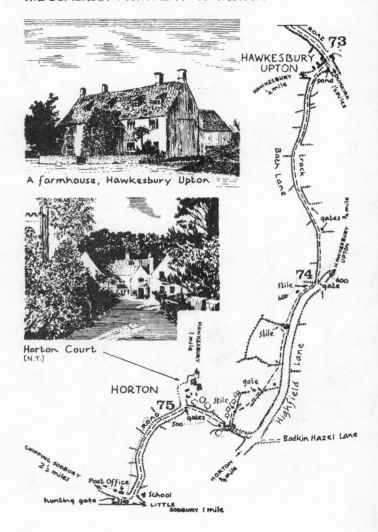

A farmhouse, Hawkesbury Upton

Horton Court
(N.T.)

HORTON

ROAD 73

HAWKESBURY
UPTON

HAWKESBURY ½ mile

pond

DUNKIRK 1¼ miles

Bath Lane

track

gates ¾ mile

HAWKESBURY UPTON ¾ mile

74

stile

600

600

gate

stile

stile

Highfield Lane

gate

stile

75

ROAD

500

gates

Badkin Hazel Lane

HAWKESBURY 1 mile

HORTON ⅓ mile

CHIPPING SODBURY 2½ miles

Post Office

hunting gate

School

LITTLE SODBURY 1 mile

Old Sodbury
Church
(above)

Doorway of
Little Sodbury
Church

HORTON to COOMB'S END

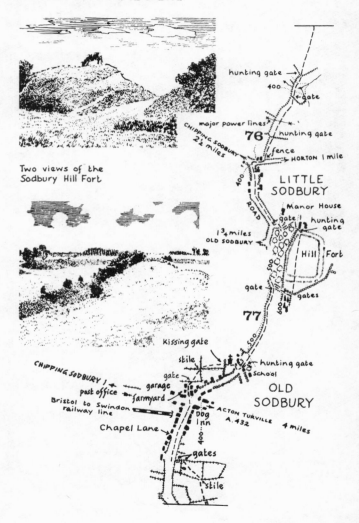

Two views of the
Sodbury Hill Fort

hunting gate
400
gate
major power lines
CHIPPING SODBURY
2½ miles
76
hunting gate
fence
HORTON 1 mile
400
**LITTLE
SODBURY**
ROAD
Manor House
gate
hunting
gate
1¾ miles
OLD SODBURY
Hill Fort
gate
gates
500
77
400
500
Kissing gate
stile
500
hunting gate
School
CHIPPING SODBURY
gate
post office
garage
farmyard
**OLD
SODBURY**
Bristol to Swindon
railway line
ACTON TURVILLE
A.432   4 miles
Chapel Lane
Dog
Inn
A
4
3
2
gates
stile

St. Mary Magdalene
Tormarton

rotund entrance lodge, Dodington Park

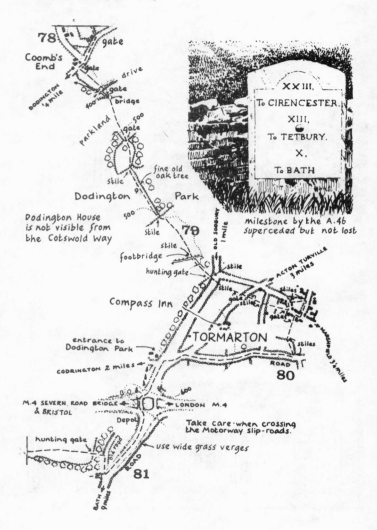

78

Coomb's
End

gate

DODINGTON ¼ mile

gate

drive

gate

400

bridge

parkland

500

gate

stile

fine old
oak tree

Dodington   Park

91

Dodington House
is not visible from
the Cotswold Way

500

stile

79

milestone by the A.46
superceded but not lost

XXIII.
To CIRENCESTER.
XIII.
To TETBURY.
X.
To BATH

stile

footbridge

hunting gate

stile

OLD SODBURY 1 mile

stile

Compass Inn

stile

gate

ACTON TURVILLE 3 miles

stiles

stile

gate

entrance to
Dodington Park

TORMARTON

stiles

CODRINGTON 2 miles

87

600

ROAD

80

M.4 SEVERN ROAD BRIDGE
& BRISTOL

LONDON M.4

Depot

Take care when crossing
the Motorway slip-roads.

hunting gate

use wide grass verges

ROAD

81

BATH
9 miles

St. Peter's
Dyrham

Dyrham Park

M.4 TO DYRHAM WOOD

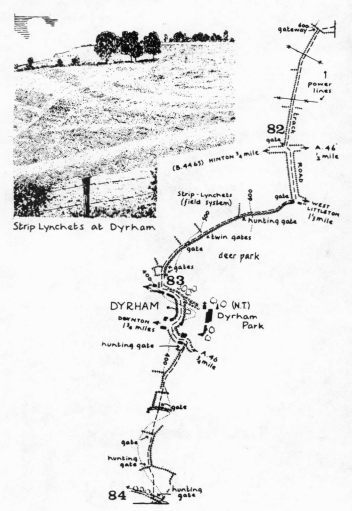

Strip Lynchets at Dyrham

600
gateway

power
lines

82
gate

track road

A.46
½ mile

(B.4465) HINTON ¾ mile

Strip-Lynchets
(field system)

600

gate

WEST
LITTLETON
1½ mile

hunting gate

twin gates

deer park

gate

gates

400

83

DYRHAM

(N.T)
Dyrham
Park

DOWNTON
1¾ miles

hunting gate

A.46
¼ mile

600

gate

gate

hunting
gate

84   **600**   hunting
gate

Cold Ashton Parish Church

The Swan Inn, Pennsylvania

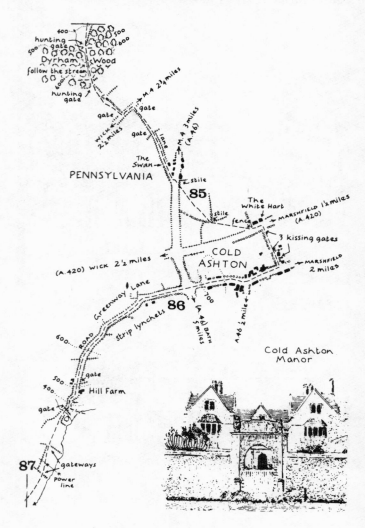

400
500
600

hunting
gate
500
600
Dyrham Wood
follow the stream

hunting
gate

gate

gate

M.4 2½ miles

gate

WICK
2½ miles

gate

lane

M.4 3 miles
(A.46)

The
Swan

PENNSYLVANIA

stile

85

stile

The
White Hart

MARSHFIELD 1½ miles
(A.420)

fence

3 kissing gates

**COLD
ASHTON**

(A.420) WICK 2½ miles

MARSHFIELD
2 miles

Greenway Lane

86

ROAD

strip lynchets

A.46
5 miles

A.46 ½ mile

BATH

600

Cold Ashton
Manor

500

gate

Hill Farm

400

gate

87

gateways

power
line

Kelston Round Hill from
Prospect Stile

The Granville Monument

HALL LANE to PROSPECT STILE

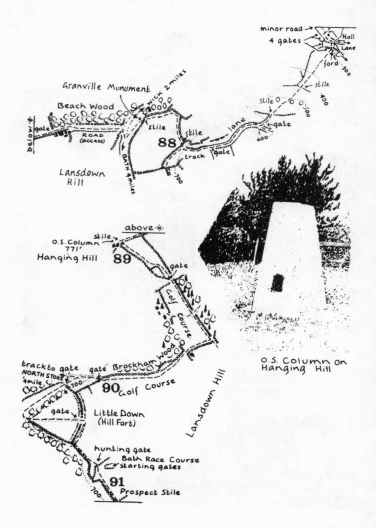

minor road →
4 gates
Hall Lane
ford 300
stile
Stile 0 400
Stile 0 500

Granville Monument
wick 2 miles
Beach Wood
gate
ROAD (access)
stile
stile
lane
gate
88
600
track gate
700
Bath 4 miles
Lansdown Hill

stile above ·×·
O.S. Column 771'
Hanging Hill **89**
gate

Golf Course

O.S. Column on Hanging Hill

track to gate gate Brockham Wood
NORTH STOKE
¼ mile 700
90 Golf Course

Lansdown Hill

gate Little Down (Hill Fort)

hunting gate
Bath Race Course
starting gates
91
700 Prospect Stile

All Saints, Upper Weston from Church Street

PROSPECT STILE to SION HILL

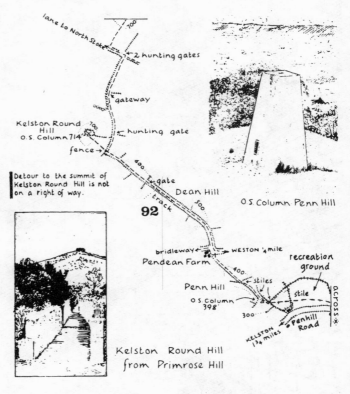

lane to North Stoke

700

2 hunting gates

gateway

Kelston Round Hill
O.S. Column 714

hunting gate

700

fence→

**Detour to the summit of
Kelston Round Hill is not
on a right of way.**

400

gate

Dean Hill

track

92

500

O.S. Column Penn Hill

bridleway   WESTON ¼ mile

Pendean Farm

recreation
ground

400

stiles

Penn Hill

stile

ACROSS ✳

O.S. Column
398

300

KELSTON
1¾ miles

Penhill
Road

Kelston Round Hill
from Primrose Hill

WESTON

93

Church
Street

squeeze
stile

kissing gate

300   Primrose Hill

ACROSS ✳

Anchor Rd

200

Church
Road

Purlewent
Drive

The Retreat (Pub)

Summerhill Rd

Sion Hill

CITY CENTRE
1½ miles

Weston Park East

300

SION HILL

Lansdown Rd
½ mile

Bath Abbey and
the Roman Baths

SION HILL to **BATH**

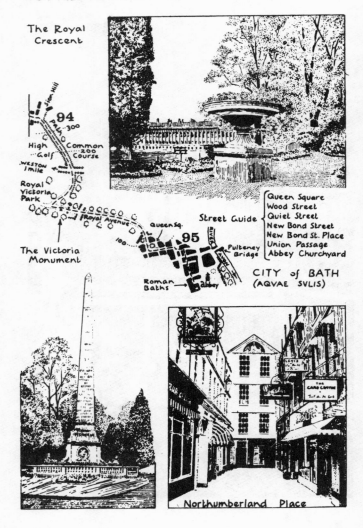

The Royal Crescent

Sion Hill

PALIO

94

300

High Golf
Common
Course
200

WESTON
1 mile

Royal Victoria Park

Royal Avenue

The Victoria Monument

Queen Sq.

100

95

Street Guide

River Avon

Pulteney Bridge

Roman Baths → Abbey

Queen Square
Wood Street
Quiet Street
New Bond Street
New Bond St. Place
Union Passage
Abbey Churchyard

CITY of BATH
(AQVAE SVLIS)

Northumberland Place

INDEX TO PLACE NAMES ON THE MAPS

WOOLSTAPLERS HALL MUSEUM,
HIGH STREET. Chipping Campden

Hill Farm near Cold Ashton

Strip lynchets on Coombe Hill above Wotton-under-Edge

SYMBOLS & ABBREVIATIONS
USED IN LARGE SCALE MAPS

Map Scale 2½" = 1 mile   North is top of every page

The route is indicated by dashes.
The number encircled being mileage
from Chipping Campden.

 Wall   Hedge   Trees   Stream or River with direction of flow.

Earthworks or steep slopes   ...400 ...300 ...200   Contours at 100' intervals

Unenclosed road or track   Buildings   Railway line

△ Ordnance Survey triangulation column

Y.H.A : Youth Hostel
N.T. : National Trust property

1 : 50,000 Ordnance Survey sheets covering the Cotswold Way

Sheet No.	Name	Map Coverage	miles
151	Stratford-upon-Avon	Chipping Campden to the Mile Drive	2½
150	Worcester and The Malverns	The Mile Drive to Winchcombe	15
163	Cheltenham and Cirencester	Pilgrim's Way to Cooper's Hill	25½
162	Gloucester and Forest of Dean	Cooper's Hill to the Somerset Monument	33¾
172	Bristol and Bath	Brackenbury Ditches to Bath	33